One Woolly Wombat

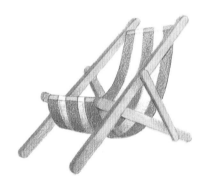

Omnibus Books
175–177 Young Street, Parkside SA 5063
an imprint of Scholastic Australia Pty Ltd (ABN11000614577)
PO Box 579, Gosford NSW 2250.
www.scholastic.com.au

Part of the Scholastic Group
Sydney • Auckland • New York • Toronto • London • Mexico City •
New Delhi • HongKong • Buenos Aires • Puerto Rico

First published in 1982.
First published in paperback in 1983.
Reprinted in 1986, 1987, 1988, 1989, 1990, 1991, 1992, 1993, 1994 (twice),
1996, 1997, 1998 (twice), 1999 (twice), 2000, 2002, 2003, 2004, 2005, 2006.
Revised edition published in 2007.
Reprinted in 2007, 2008 (three times), 2010, 2011.
This edition published in 2012.
Reprinted in 2013, 2014 (twice), 2015 (three times).

National Library of Australia Cataloguing-in-Publication entry

Argent, Kerry.
One woolly wombat.
For preschool children.
ISBN 978 1 86291 969 3.
1. Animals — Australia — Juvenile literature.
2. Counting — Juvenile literature. I. Title.
513.211

Kerry Argent used colour pencil and some watercolour wash for the illustrations in this book.
Typeset in Abadi MT Condensed and Curlz MT.
Printed by Tien Wah Press (Pte) Ltd.

Scholastic Australia's policy, in association with Tien Wah Press, is to use papers
that are renewable and made efficiently from wood grown in sustainable forests,
so as to minimise its environmental footprint.

10 9 8 7   15 16 17 18 19 20 / 0

One Woolly Wombat

Kerry Argent

An Omnibus Book from Scholastic Australia

1

One woolly wombat
sunning
by the sea

Two cuddly koalas
sipping
gumnut tea

3

Three warbling magpies
waking up
the sun

4

Four thumping kangaroos
dancing
just for fun

5

Five pesky platypuses
splashing
with their feet

6

Six cheeky possums
looking for
a treat

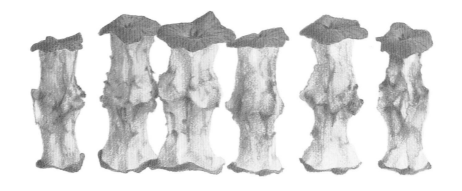

7

Seven emus running ...
in and out
the bush

8

Eight spiky echidnas
eating ants —
whoosh

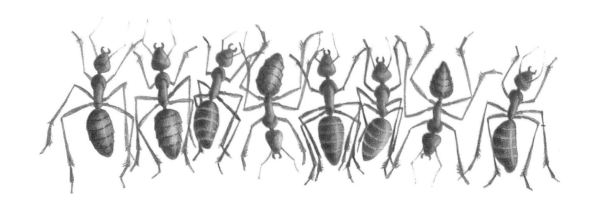

9

Nine hungry goannas
wondering
what to cook

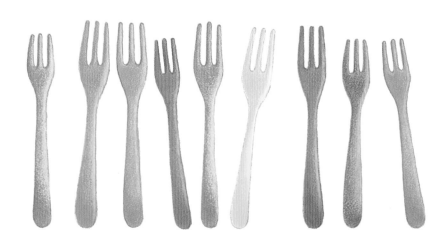

10

Ten giggly kookaburras
writing
riddle books

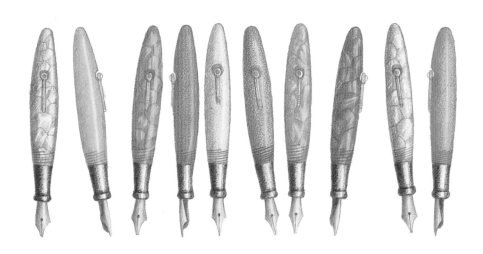

11

Eleven dizzy dingoes
twirling
with their paws

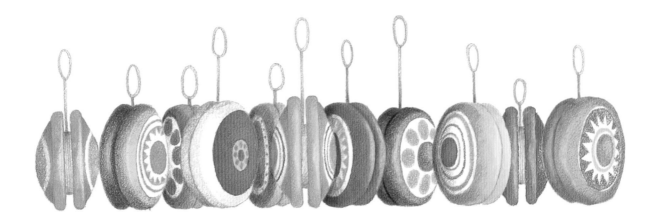

12

Twelve crazy cockatoos
counting
on their claws

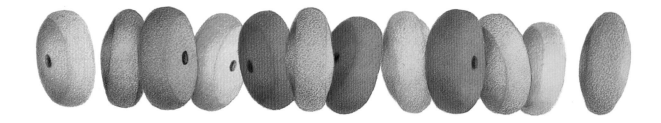

13

Thirteen hopping mice
picking
desert pea

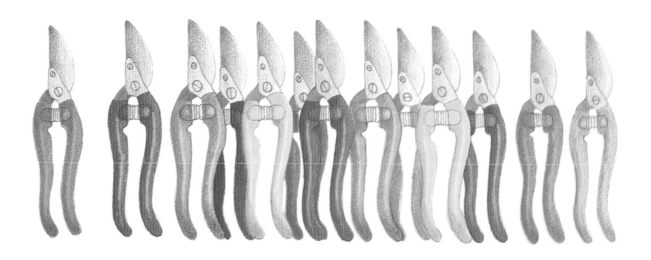

14

Fourteen slick seals
heading out
to sea